FAT CA

Colour Collection

from the **Sunday Express** £3.50

I've known Fat Cat since he was born in 1979… that makes him 10 years old, or 70 in cat years! When I revealed this to him recently, he was quite alarmed to discover that he was 'suddenly a pensioner'!

He seems to have recovered from the shock, and continues to make life difficult for his owners, most birds, assorted dogs, and of course me, as you can see from the opposite page! One wonders, with some trepidation, what he will get up to in the next 10 years. I'm sure he'll still be going strong by the time he's 20 or 140!!! Can you imagine how cantankerous he'll be by then?

The cartoons in this book have been selected from ones previously published in the Sunday Express.

I hope you enjoy them
Best Wishes

Mike Atkinson

For Ben

32

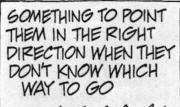

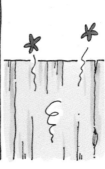

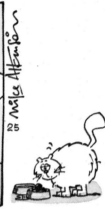

IT'S ALWAYS A MISTAKE TO GO OUT WITH THEM IN THE CAR...

WHEN HE'S BEEN WATCHING MOTOR-RACING ON T.V.!

YAWN

SOME DAYS IT'S ALL GO!

THEY'RE GOING OUT FOR THE EVENING...

I DON'T LIKE IT WHEN THE HOUSE IS EMPTY AND I'M ALL ALONE!

WELL, NOT **QUITE** ALONE...

I'VE GOT MY SUPPER-DISH!

THAT'S PUSSY-CAT FOR 'I'M HOME'

WHAT ARE YOU DOING? YOU'VE BEEN SITTING THERE FOR HOURS

I WOULD HAVE THOUGHT IT WAS OBVIOUS...

I'M WAITING FOR OPENING TIME!

WHAT AN AWFUL NIGHT!

ONE FALSE MOVE AND THE SWEATER GETS IT!

MAYBE WE SHOULD LET HIM STAY IN TONIGHT

A VICTORY FOR COMMON SENSE I THINK!

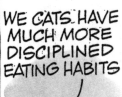

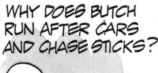

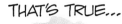

JUST IN TIME BY THE LOOKS OF IT...

IN FAVOURABLE CONDITIONS, I CAN HEAR THE RUSTLE OF CHOCOLATE WRAPPINGS AT THREE HUNDRED YARDS!

A DESPERATE SITUATION...

CALLS FOR DESPERATE MEASURES!

PLONK!

THAT WAS MY FAMOUS, BUT VERY RISKY 'CONFUSE-A-CANINE' PLOY!

HERE COMES THAT PEDIGREE BEAGLE FROM NUMBER SEVENTEEN...

HE'S A TERRIFIC SNOB SO I'M QUITE SAFE...

...HE ONLY CHASES PEDIGREE CATS!

DON'T WORRY... I'M NOT GOING TO POUNCE ON YOU

I MAKE IT A RULE NEVER TO CHASE BIRDS WITH MIGRATION-LAG!

RUMBLE
NO... NOT NOW!

RUMBLE RUMBLE
DIDN'T YOU HEAR ME... I SAID NO!

RUMBLE RUMBLE RUMBLE

SOMETIMES MY STOMACH JUST WON'T TAKE NO FOR AN ANSWER!

EEEK!

A MOUSE IS IT? DON'T PANIC... I'LL GET HIM!

A SPIDER! THERE'S A SPIDER IN THE BATH!

SHE'S RIGHT... AND IT'S A BIG BLACK HORRIBLE ONE WITH HAIRY LEGS!

ACCORDING TO MY RECENT SURVEY, TWO OUT OF THREE PEOPLE ARE CAT LOVERS!

I HATE DOGS!

IN FACT THEY DRIVE ME UP THE WALL...

FREQUENTLY!

I LIKE TO EAT AT LEAST THREE LARGE MEALS A DAY IF POSSIBLE

AFTER ALL...

ONE NEVER KNOWS WHEN ANOREXIA MAY STRIKE!